SAM

The Adirondack Railroad Cat

BY

Nancy A. Douglas

ILLUSTRATED BY

Valerie Patterson

North Country Books, Inc.
Utica, New York

SAM, THE ADIRONDACK RAILROAD CAT

Graphic Design and Electronic Page Assembly
by Maren Miles
Red Pine Computer Services
HCR01, Box 86, Malone, NY 12953

Edited by Carolyn Tulloch

Second Printing 1997

Third Printing 2004

Library of Congress Cataloging-in-Publication Data

Douglas, Nancy A., 1936-
    Sam, the Adirondack Railroad cat / by Nancy A.
Douglas
Illustrated by Valerie Patterson
        p. cm.
    Summary: Sam becomes the mascot of the Adirondack
Railroad.
    ISBN 0-925168-28-9
    1. Cats—Fiction. 2. Railroads—Fiction. 3. Moun-
tains—Fiction. 4. Stories in rhyme. I. Patterson, Valerie,
1963- III. II. Title
PZ8,3.D748Sam   1994
    [E]-dc20   94-7690
                                                         CIP
                                                          AC

North Country Books, Inc.
Utica, New York

Foreword

I was introduced to Sam while working as a volunteer for the Adirondack Centennial Railroad during the summer of 1992. One day, in the small gift shop at Thendara Station, Sam was placed before me on the counter with the comment, "Nancy, I would like you to meet Sam." My response was, "*Sam, the Adirondack Railroad Cat*. That sounds like a great title for a children's book."

The idea was enthusiastically accepted by my artist friend, Val, and we were on our way.

In February of '93, while the book was in progress, we learned that Sam would soon be moving to Ohio. The decision to proceed with the book was made considering Sam's place in the history of the Adirondack Centennial Railroad and to honor this remarkable cat.

Sam, this book is dedicated to you. Thanks for the inspiration to create it!

We miss you Sam!

Thendara Station is the home
    Of the Adirondack train.
Here, once lived a cat named Sam
    And this was his domain.

This quaint, old railroad station
    Was the place that Sam called home.
At night, when folks were sound asleep,
    Around the tracks he'd roam.

Sam became an Adirondacker
    In June of '92.
He didn't wander there alone;
    He brought his owners, too.

They moved into Thendara,
    South of Old Forge, just a mile.
In this friendly, small community
    They planned to stay awhile.

They were there to run a railroad,
    A short excursion run
In the Central Adirondacks;
    They thought it would be fun.

Sam quickly made a lot of friends,
　　So lovable was he,
And, more than that, this railroad cat
　　Had personality.

To help folks get acquainted
　　With this dignified feline,
There in Thendara Station,
　　Sam's friends put up this sign.

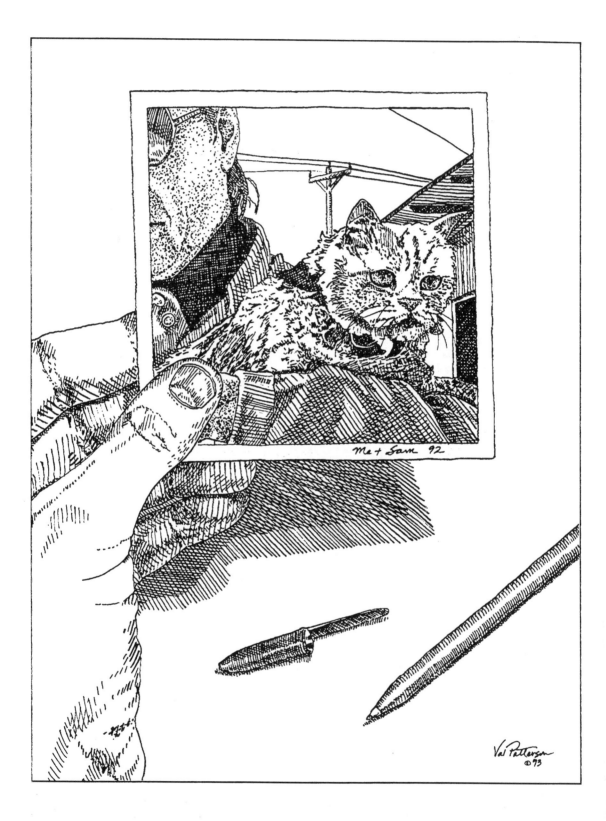

Me + Sam 92

Val Patterson
©93

This Railroad cat, you understand,
    Was really quite a ham.
He posed for all photographers—
    This charming cat named Sam.

Sam was official mascot
    For the Adirondack train;
And if you wonder what he did,
    Allow me to explain.

Sam had a knack for sleeping;
    T'was what he did the best.
He'd jump on the display case
    And have a peaceful rest.

Sam enjoyed the station gift shop!
There was so much to see:
Train souvenirs of many types
And great activity.

Val Patterson
©'93

Sam liked sitting in the station
  To wait for his train ride.
He'd be off to Minnehaha
  Through the mountain countryside.

Sam even rode the engine
    As the train made its round trip.
He liked to ride almost as much
    As rolling in catnip.

The beautiful Moose River
    Can be seen right from the train.
Sam liked to sit on the left side
    Next to the windowpane.

Sam had his own bandanas;
 Some were red, the others blue.
He wore a clean one every day
 Since he had quite a few.

Around the ticket office
 Sam easily could find
Someone to hold and pet him.
 His friends were very kind.

This grand hotel, Van Auken's Inne,
    Is right across the street.
And Sam liked going over there
    To get a special treat.

Scraps from the hotel kitchen
    He'd discover in his dish.
You know he was delighted
    When he found a piece of fish!

Val Patterson
©'93

Sam loved to go off hunting.
    He thought it oh, so nice
To sneak up on and maybe catch
    Some Adirondack mice.

He very often tracked them down
    With skills that were sublime;
We like to think Sam was so good
    He'd get them every time.

Now we have to say good-bye
    To Sam, the railroad cat.
We were happy to have known him;
    You can be sure of that.

For folks who did not meet him,
    What we hope this book will do
Is help you know this cat named Sam,
    And learn to love him, too!

The Adirondack Railroad cat,
    This Sam we all adore,
Has earned a place in history
    And New York State folklore.

And maybe if we're lucky,
    Sam will return again
And climb aboard and ride with us—
    The Adirondack train.

Meet *Mountain Trillium*

Nancy A. Douglas was born in Niagara Falls, NY. She is a retired elementary teacher, currently living in the Adirondack Park. "I loved trains even as a child when my father was an engineer on the New York Central Railroad. The Adirondack Railroad has been 'an old friend' since the early 1950's."

Valerie Patterson grew up along the St. Lawrence River in Ogdensburg, NY. She now lives in Whippleville, NY and spends much of her free time in the Adirondacks, hiking, skiing and painting. When she's not playing in the mountains, she's teaching art to elementary school students.

Maren, 'Marty', Miles comes from Massena, NY. She has been a lover of the Adirondacks most of her life—hiking, climbing, canoeing, camping, and skiing. She retired from teaching physical education in June 1993 and has since started a computer business, Red Pine Computer Services. She lives in Duane, NY.